Wade Through the Pandemic

Pandemic

By Wade and Joshua Williams

Illustrated by Sergio Drumond

Dedication

This book is dedicated to my mom Dr. Alfreda Williams (Wade's Grandma) and Coronavirus survivor. Dr. Williams is the most kindhearted, selfless, non-judgmental person I have ever gotten the pleasure to know. She is a wife, dedicated mother of 3, grandmother of 2, and retired teacher of 40 years. Dr. Williams always puts others before herself, oftentimes sacrificing her own needs for others' wants and always placing the family first.

One day my daddy picked me up from school.

He told me that he, mommy and I were going to hang out for awhile at home.

Daddy said that from now on we can only meet people over the phone.

I asked daddy "why does it have to be just us".

He said it is because of the coronavirus.

The coronavirus is a tiny germ that if it gets in your body can make you very sick.

So to do our part, if we cough or sneeze we have to do it on our arm, quick.

You have to put on your mask to stay strong

And wash your hands often to the ABC Song.

Mommy has a baby in her belly. My little sister is coming soon.

I know she will be pretty with big eyes like the moon.

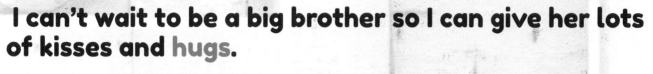

I can't wait to be a big brother so I can give her lots of kisses and hugs.

Also I can't wait to show her my collection of bugs.

The days go by and it's just mommy, daddy, and me all day and night.

I want to go outside and play with kids but daddy says the time is not right.

Papa had to take grandmama to the hospital because she could not breathe.

Daddy gets upset and starts chomping his teeth.

I am sad because grandmama is my one true friend I love.

Daddy gets on his knees and prays to God up above.

Time passes and grandmama is doing better,
While mommy, daddy and I are still together
everyday practicing my letters.

Then late one night I heard mommy scream loud.

She said the baby is coming! We need to go now!

Mommy and daddy rushed me to my auntie's home.

We were moving so fast they forgot my brush and my comb.

We waited and waited. It seemed like all the time passed in the world.

We waited and waited, still no baby girl.

Then the next morning I got a call from daddy.

He showed me my sister and she was beautiful and happy.

The next day I saw my sister for the first-time. Mommy named her Celine.

She is sweet, cries a lot, beautiful and clean.

I gave my baby sister a nickname of "CC"

And show her off to my auntie's and GG.

I help mommy and daddy with her by shaking her bottles and throwing her dirty diapers in the trash.

Whenever me and daddy go outside, we still wear our mask.

As time goes by daddy goes back to work and mommy moves out of state and gets her own place.

Me and CC go to live with grandmama and papa at their place.

We have fun at grandmama house playing, reading, watching cartoons and laughing.

She is my best friend and mommy and daddy come to see me every weekend.

My aunties give me what I want whenever I ask.

And whenever we go out papa yells, "Put on a mask".

CC is getting bigger each and every day.

I'm so happy to have her. I show videos of her when I'm on the phone with Uncle J.

Life is different since the virus but everything will be OK.

When you get upset just close you eyes, count to 10 and you will have a better day.

Or go outside for a walk with a trusted adult and don't forget your shoes...

I'm wading through this pandemic and you can, too.

Wade

and Celine

CPSIA information can be obtained
at www.ICGtesting.com
Printed in the USA
LVHW072026191120
672181LV00002B/78